the dumplings

by Fred Lucky

tempo
books | Grosset & Dunlap
Publishers, New York

ISBN: 0-448-12466-1
A Tempo Books Original
Tempo Books is registered in the U.S. Patent Office
Published simultaneously in Canada
Printed in the United States of America

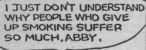

ANGIE, TODAY'S SATURDAY! FORGET ALL THAT!

HERE'S FIVE BUCKS. GO DOWNTOWN, DO SOME SHOPPING AND HAVE YOURSELF A BALL.

JOEY SURE KNOWS HOW TO KEEP HIS LADY HAPPY.

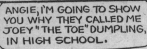

YOU LOOK ESPECIALLY LOVELY TONIGHT, ANGIE.

THANK YOU. I THINK SO, TOO.

A LITTLE VANITY IN A BEAUTIFUL WOMAN IS CUTE.

ANGIE, DON'T SIT ON THE TERRACE LIKE THAT, IT'S DANGEROUS.

DO YOU WANT TO CAUSE A COLLISION?

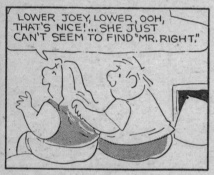